All the work in this volume appears in its original
form and is intended to expose the evolution of
Berni Wrightson, from his fanzine days to the
present. The "Frankenstein" illustrations in the
portfolio section are his most recent work and
are alternatives to the illustrations that will appear in his forthcoming book. I couldn't bear to
think they would never see print.
—F.B.

The Mother of Pearl Publishing Co.
P.O. Box 5, Parkville Station
Brooklyn, NY 11204

ISBN 0-937848-00-X

CONTENTS

Dark Comedy
A Decade with Berni Wrightson

We entered the Baltimore cemetery under slate-gray skys pregnant with rain. We trod an asphalt path that Berni had walked countless times since childhood—usually at night, usually alone. It had been instrumental in shaping both his life, and his art. I would have known that even if his rambling conversation hadn't hinted it as we strolled among the graves, for Berni was at home here. The gaunt lanes of skeletal trees and towering, granite-faced crypts embraced him like old friends. There had been times in his life when only the silence of tombstones and quiet lawns could be trusted with the special problems inherent in a young artist's life. It was apparent that these had listened many times to his, even as they were listening now. . .

It had been an unusual year.

Berni had made a major move to a strange town, faced critical decisions about his art, fallen intermittently in and out of love, lost his father to cancer and moved back to New York again all within a few short months. I had embarked on a new writing career, redefined old friendships and was trying to make some sense of my chaotic life. And through it all, Berni and I had held each other up, laughed at the recklessness, sighed at the losses and strengthened a friendship I shall value always.

"It used to be an open cemetery," he was saying, squinting up at the grumbling overcast. "But teenagers started vandalizing the place so they fenced it in." I glanced across at his chiseled features and saw a thousand grave-choked comic panels reflected in his eyes. "They put guard dogs in here at night to keep the people out." I thought about the graveyard scene in Val Lewton's LEOPARD MAN. "That could be a little hairy," I replied, "if you got trapped in here."

"Oh, I did once!" Berni exclaimed proudly.

"You're kidding!"

"I was right here in the middle of it one night, strollin' along gawkin' at the moon. I think it was Halloween. I remember hearing them coming for me, howling and barking over the hills. . ."

"Lord, what did you do?"

"I climbed a tree."

I was both chilled and envious. I have always thought Berni and I would have had a great childhood together—instead of having to watch horror movies, read E.C. Comics, and learn to draw separately. Berni could have taught me much. But that wouldn't happen until 1968 when I walked into Jeff Jones' New York apartment with my new bride and saw a Byronic young man in jeans and sweater slouched on a sofa with a drawing board on his lap. "Bruce, this is Berni Wrightson, he's just started working for Nation-Periodicals. . ."

One look and it was obvious why National had snatched him up. That portfolio of early drawings beside him—the first Wrightson art I had ever seen—was truly staggering, all the more so for his tender years. I remember taking Jeff aside later and whispering with facetious envy, "How're we gonna get *rid* of this guy?"

Berni affected all our work in some way, whether in actual application or just in the enthusiasm that flowed from his brush. Probably that was his greatest contribution—just looking at the immense love and care that went into each panel. Like Frazetta—The Godfather—Berni drew like he'd never worked at it at all, like it was the most natural thing in the world to have all this wonderful stuff just appear magically on a blank page before him—while the rest of us sketched and erased and scratched and fumed and sweated blood.

But then, we didn't have the cemetery. . .

We stopped before his favorite gravestone and Berni pointed it out to me; a young girl in a cloak and hood somberly guarding the sleeping form beneath her. Vaughn Bode's face jumped into my thoughts, his death still fresh in all our minds. I pictured him sitting there on the living room floor of the house he and Jeff shared in Woodstock. He was leaning forward intensely, as were all the other guests, listening spellbound as Berni unfolded a ghastly ghost story under flickering candle light at the "best Halloween party of the century." Berni had absolutely no idea how the story would end, nor was he supposed to. It was only a ploy to set a grisly mood and get everyone's blood pumping while I sneaked quietly out the back door, tip-toed around the side of the house and waited by the louvered entrance to the living room. We had planned it hours in advance and Jeff was the only other person in on it.

"But I don't know any ghost stories!" Berni had said.

"Just make-up a bunch of scary stuff," I told him, "I'll burst in before you have to think of an ending."

It worked only too well.

I found a length of black cloth outside on the porch, placed it over my head, waited until Berni reached a particularly hoary passage in his narrative, then burst through the louvers with a scream.

One guy almost jumped into the fireplace. Two

girls shrieked and fell over backward throwing their drinks skyward. I whipped off the cloth cheerfully and looked at Berni. He was pale and wide-eyed. "What's the matter, man?" Berni swallowed. "Jesus, I got so caught up in my own story," he said, "I forgot you were back there!"

Doubtless, that is the secret of Berni's art: involvement. It wouldn't scare the crap out of you if it wasn't scaring the crap out of Berni.

We stopped on the cemetery path and Berni reached down and picked up a flat stone. "Looking for snakes."

It wasn't the first time. Once, in Kansas City, we spent an entire afternoon scouring the large field behind my apartment looking for serpents, lifting stone after stone in 90 degree weather. "What's the largest snake you ever found doing this?" I asked. Berni considered thoughtfully. "In all the years I've been catching snakes," he said, "I've never found a single one under a stone."

I broke into laughter and fell back on my ass. "Then why the hell are we doing this?" Berni looked at me. "Somebody once told me that's how you find them."

He *had* collected many snakes, though. At one time or another there was always a rainbow boa or corn snake in an aquarium on top of Berni's TV or bookshelf. I even witnessed this strange ritual one day when Berni suggested we look for water snakes in the creek in my back yard. I'd never seen any water snakes in the creek but then I'd never really looked for them. I found that there is a real art to it. Berni pointed out two beautiful specimens from the bridge spanning the creek that looked to me for all the world like reeds waving in the current. Then, with me guiding from the bridge, he descending to the rushing waters, waded across the tumbled stone and shot a hand beneath the surface. An instant later that same hand resurfaced lashed by rust-colored coils. It was a plucky little water snake too. It didn't want any part of being man-handled and tried to bite Berni twice. After a suitable period of admiration we let him go.

Collecting didn't stop with reptiles, at least not live ones. Dinosaurs are an even more sought after item by Berni, anything from the two inch plastic and rubber models you can get at the local Woolworths to the enormous lumbering giants Aurora put out a few years back. Rubber dragons, Egyptian stone replicas and any *really* neat toys are also much valued. But don't be misled. It has to be the right kind of toy. There's a real selectivity about all this, as fellow toy collector Mike Kaluta will tell you. Just any little dimestore trinket won't do. It must be real "Junque." It's an acquired art. You've either got it or you ain't.

Rain drops pelted down erratically as we

WRIGHTSON
'69

neared the exit gate. It was time to leave the cemetery as it would soon be time to leave Baltimore and thus end a period of close proximity for Berni and I. I had enjoyed it immensely but perhaps it was for the best; when two goof-offs like Berni and I get together nothing really enduring gets done. In Kansas City, when Berni had an apartment close to mine, the day would usually begin with Berni phoning up and saying, "Hello, my name is Berni Wrightson. I am an artist. Feed me." Then, we'd drive up to the House of Pancakes (perfecting our Popeye impressions all the way, of course) and drink coffee and bullshit for as long as we could delay getting to work. Then, we'd go back to Berni's place and I'd fool around with my stuff and Berni would daub paint awhile and we'd decide it was time for lunch. Lunch was mostly at Denny's because they had a waitress named Molly who was stacked almost as good as their pancakes.

After lunch we'd go to the hobby shops and debate about whether we *really* needed another plastic skull and by then the day was shot. Oh well, we'll work tomorrow. . . . Yeah, sure.

Not that we haven't worked well "together." I have been told repeatedly that my story JENIFER is the best thing I ever wrote for the Warren books. Maybe. But I'd be kidding myself if I didn't admit that without Berni's incredible graphics the thing would have probably gone unnoticed. It's been said before: a good artist can *make* a mediocre story—or wreck a great one. I've been fortunate enough to work with some really great artists among which Berni is certainly on the front line.

Through the nearly ten years of our friendship, little isolated highlights pop like strobic flashes across my mind—as nutty as the Warner Brothers cartoons we revere: Berni doing his Karloff impression on the elevator on 79th Street; Berni running around my back yard like a gibbon, sending my poor wife into gales of laughter; Berni emerging from the bathroom wearing his CREATURE FROM THE BLACK LAGOON mask; Berni sitting transfixed before the TV absorbed for the hundredth time in BRIDE OF FRANKENSTEIN; Berni waxing enthusiastic about the "greatest horror film of them all," THE TEXAS CHAINSAW MASSACRE . . . or telling you how terrific Graham Ingles was . . . or how we're going to make this really great movie someday . . . or just sitting there over his coffee cup reflecting on why we're here and what it all means . . .

We left the cemetery behind us and headed for Berni's mother's house a few blocks away. We'd reflected enough. It was time to get on to New York—on to other stories, other adventures. There's a whole new decade of memories waiting to be filled.

I can hardly wait.

Bruce Jones
Overland Park, Kansas
April 3, 1977

WRIGHTSON '71

9

OUR CHILDREN WILL BE HUMAN AGAIN?

THAT'S RIGHT! OUR GENERATION WILL BE FORGOTTEN LIKE A BAD DREAM! OUR CHILDREN WILL RESEMBLE OUR PARENTS--AND THE PARENTS OF THESE FEMALES...

BOTH THEIR MINDS AND THEIR BODIES WILL BE NORMAL!

HOPE, LIKE A SPRING BREEZE, GIVES NEW LIFE TO THE EARTH. THE INHABITANTS OF SUBSTATION TWELVE EMERGE INTO THE LIGHT, BUILDING, REPAIRING...

NURSERY PROJECT HOPE

...CAPTURING MORE FEMALES FOR THE BREEDING LABS, BELOW, UNTIL ONE DAY...

COME ON, NOW! I WON'T HURT YOU... SEE, RICK! THEY CAN BE TAMED!

RICK! RICK! COME BELOW! HURRY!

THE CHILDREN? BUT THAT'S IMPOSSIBLE, AFTER ONLY SIX WEEKS...

YOU'LL SEE... AND THEN YOU'LL WISH YOU HADN'T...

IT'S GONE, RICK! OUR LAST HOPE! GONE!

WHAT DO YOU MEAN? WHAT ABOUT THE FEMALES? ARE THEY ALRIGHT?

I DESTROYED THEM!

DESTROYED THEM!?!

WHY? WHY DIDN'T THE SERUM WORK?

OH, IT WORKED, ALL RIGHT! THE CHILDREN RESEMBLE THEIR GRANDPARENTS... BUT, THE FEMALES WERE MUTANTS, AND WE DIDN'T KNOW IT!

...BUT, WE KNEW THEIR MINDS WERE...

THEIR MINDS WERE PERFECTLY NORMAL! IT WAS THEIR BODIES THAT CHANGED!

BREEDING LAB

THEY ONLY LOOKED HUMAN BECAUSE THE RADIATION CHANGED THEM COMPLETELY — EVEN MORE THAN IT CHANGED US!

THEY WERE ACTUALLY...

MUTANT TOADS!

BUT, ⁊CHOKE⁊ BUT WHAT HAPPENED TO THE HUMANS?

DID THEY CHANGE INTO...

ATTA GIRL! COME ON NOW! HERE'S YOUR DINNER...

NOTHING FOR ME TO SAY BUT... THE END

THE TASK...

WRIGHTSON '70

I STAND NOW, STRAIGHT AND STILL, MY SHOULDERS GLISTENING AND MY FOREARMS DAMP...I GAZE DOWN, MY IMAGINARY VICTOR'S FOOT ON THE WHITE BELLY OF THE VANQUISHED...AND ONCE AGAIN THE EMPTINESS FILLS ME.

I TURN MY GAZE SKYWARD, MOMENTARILY FASCINATED BY THE BLACKER AURA OF NIGHT THAT SURROUNDS A STAR...ONCE AGAIN, MY RAGE TASTES BITTER IN MY THROAT...

I MOVE AWAY, SICKENED, AND ABANDON MY TASK... ONCE AGAIN...

...THREE TIMES BEFORE HAS MY STOMACH CURDLED THUS... THREE TIMES BEFORE HAVE I TURNED TO LEAVE THE MADNESS SMOULDERING BEHIND ME ...AND NOW, FOUR TIMES HAS MY WEAPON BETRAYED ME... THE WEIGHT OF ITS COSMIC REBIRTH AND THINGS A THOUSAND TIMES DEAD FLOWS INTO ITS WOODEN HAFT AND SHINY, STAINED BLADE.

...ONCE AGAIN, ITS HEFT DOUBLES, TRIPLES, INCREASES WITH THE SPEED OF A SUDDEN MEMORY. ITS WEIGHT HAS BECOME THAT OF THE LIFE IT HAS MOST RECENTLY TAKEN...BUT, MY THOUGHTS OF DESERTION HAVE MADE IT SO... ONCE AGAIN!

IT'S TOO LATE TO RE-CONSIDER... TOO LATE FOR THE TREMENDOUS FORCE OF WILL THAT WILL REVERT IT TO A WEAPON OF RIGHT...THE CHARMED AXE PULLS ME TO THE GROUND AND THREATENS TO WRENCH THE LIMB FROM ITS SOCKET...ONCE AGAIN...

16

...I CAN FEEL THE MUSCLES STRETCHING...HEAR THE TORTURED NERVES AND TENDONS SCREAMING FOR RELEASE...AND THROUGH MY PAIN AND MY RAGE, I SEE A HEADSMAN'S DEEP-SCARRED BLOCK, SMELL ITS BLACK STAINS AND HEAR A VOICE CRYING, *"REPRIEVE! REPRIEVE!"*...

I SEE THE THRONE ROOM IN LATE AFTERNOON, ITS SHADOWS REACHING FAR AWAY INTO OBSCURE DISTANCE...I SEE THE WIZENED, BEARDED FACE OF THE COURT WARLOCK AND HEAR HIS CRACKING, THICK VOICE...

YOU'VE CHEATED THE HEADSMAN, BUT YOU'VE YET TO EARN YOUR LIFE...

...I HEAR A TALE OF BRAVE MEN NOW DEAD AND FIVE BEASTS IN A DARK FOREST...I HEAR OF A TASK, A LABOR...THE REWARD FOR WHICH WILL BE MY LIFE.

...I HEAR A GREAT HOWLING SONG, THE LYRICS SO OBSCENELY BEAUTIFUL, THE RHYTHM AND FLOW SO TERRIFYING, THAT I SWOON WITH HORROR, LEST I LOOSE HOLD AND SLIP INTO THE MAD NETHER-WORLD FROM WHENCE COMES *...THIS WAR AXE!*

ALL THE FIRES OF HELL FORGE ITS SHACKLE TO MY WRIST...I AM IMPRISONED BY MY OWN WEAPON, SOMEHOW PLEDGED TO THE UNIVERSE TO COMPLETE MY TASK...I MUST SLAY FIVE UNHOLY BEINGS BEFORE I AM FREE...

THE SORCEROR'S EYES BURN WITH THE FLAMES OF LUNACY AND A DROP OF SPITTLE GLISTENS ON HIS LIPS AS HE SPEAKS...

I CANNOT TELL YOU WHAT MANNER OF CREATURES THESE ARE, FOR INDEED, I KNOW NOT THAT MYSELF...BUT THEY WERE BROUGHT FORTH LONG AGONE BY VILE WIZARDRY OF THE DARKEST SORT, AND SO MUST THEY PERISH. THE BLADE WHICH IMPRISONS YOUR ARM AND YEA! YOUR VERY SOUL WILL CARRY YOU THROUGH YOUR TASK. YOU ARE A SLAYER OF OF BEASTS, NOW. GO, AND RETURN NOT TILL YOUR MISSION IS DONE!

I HEAR A LOW LAUGH AND INHALE THE STENCH OF ALL-EVIL AND I FIGHT FOR MY LIFE. MY AXE DESCENDS IN WIDE, SCREAMING ARCS, SWINGING LIGHT AND EASY AS A POINIARD, YET STRIKING WITH THE FORCE OF A CATAPULT...

FOR THE FIRST TIME, MY SOUL WITHERS AND I TURN AWAY FROM THE BEATEN, RED THING ON THE GROUND, VOWING TO ABANDON THIS UNHOLY TASK FOREVER. FOR THE FIRST TIME, I AM PULLED DOWN BY THE WEIGHT OF WORLDS LONG DEAD...

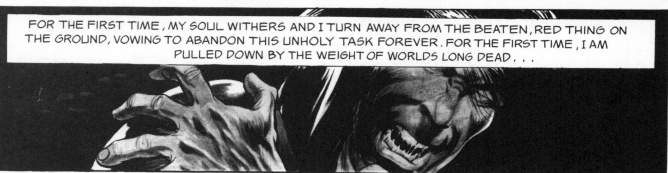

AND NOW, FOR THE THIRD TIME, I AM FACED WITH THE CHOICE OF GIVING UP AND DYING THIS SLOW, PAINFUL DEATH OR CONTINUING ON WITH MY LABOR, AT LEAST HAVING A FIGHTING CHANCE TO LIVE...

BUT THE CHOICE IS NOT THAT SIMPLE...I UNDERSTAND...FEEL, MORE THAN KNOW, WHAT THESE BEASTS ARE...THEIR HORRID COSMIC LINK WITH THE FATE OF FUTURE HUMANITY AND THE SOULS OF PAST AGES...I MUST GO ON—I MUST FINISH THIS TASK, DREADFUL THOUGH IT IS...

I DECIDE QUICKLY, CURSING MYSELF THE WHILE, BUT THE PAIN IS CONSUMMATE...WERE IT ONLY THE PROSPECT OF LOSING A STRONG ARM, I WOULD SUFFER IT TO BE SO, FOR HAVE I NOT ANOTHER, EQUALLY AS MIGHTY...

WEAKLY, I STAGGER ERECT...MY STRENGTH GRADUALLY RETURNING... AND MY STRENGTH OF PURPOSE RENEWED...

I WALK INTO THE MOONLIT FOREST, MY HEAD CLEAR AND MY FEET SILENT. MY TASK IS MORE THAN HALF DONE . . . TWO BEASTS REMAIN . . . TWO FOUL UNLIVES MUST BE TAKEN BEFORE THIS SHACKLE FALLS FROM MY ARM, FOREVER.

THERE ARE NO SOUNDS IN THIS WOOD. NO BREEZE SINGS THROUGH ITS LOFTY BOUGHS . . . NO SMALL HUNTING CREATURES RUSTLE ITS LEAF CARPETED FLOOR . . . SILENCE . . . BUT WAIT! *THERE* IS A NOISE!

IT IS THE GURGLING OF A SPRING, WELLING UP FROM THE DEPTHS OF THE FOREST'S VAST, ORGANIC CELLAR . . . ITS FINEST DRAUGHT, BUBBLING, WAITING TO BE QUAFFED . . . AN OFFER OF REFRESHMENT FROM THIS FINE, GRACIOUS HOST TO A WEARY, FOOT-SORE VISITOR . . .

I KNEEL AND SLAKE MY THIRST IN THE FOREST'S BLOOD, DRAWING NEW STRENGTH FROM ITS PURITY, AS THE PRIMITIVES DRAW STRENGTH AND VALOR FROM THE BLOOD OF THEIR FOES . . .

. . . A MOVEMENT DISTRACTS MY EYE . . . AND THEN, A SOUND . . . FIRST, A HEARTBEAT, THEN A SOFT TREAD, THEN A LONG, LABORED BREATH.

. . . I RISE SLOWLY AND MOVE TO INVESTIGATE, MATCHING MY STEALTH TO THAT OF THE UNSEEN TRAVELER.

. . . I PART THE LEAFY WALL THAT SEPARATES US AND I SEE . . . I SEE AND MY SOUL IS BLASTED BY THE ICY, BURNING WINDS OF HELL . . .

TO LOOK UPON THIS CREATURE IS TO KNOW...TO KNOW OF ITS FOUL, UNHOLY ORIGINS...THE IMPOSSIBLE UNION OF MAN AND BEAST...THE OFFSPRING, A MANIFESTATION OF THE WORST IN BOTH...THIS OGRE WEARS ITS SOUL LIKE A CLOAK...

THE HORROR OF MY FIRST IMPRESSION SUBSIDES...IT IS REPLACED NOW BY A NEED TO DESTROY...AN OVERPOWERING SENSE OF RIGHTEOUSNESS...I WANT MORE THAN LIFE TO RID THE EARTH OF THIS THING NEVER MEANT TO BE...THE MOTHER, EARTH, WHO CRINGES AT THE TOUCH OF ITS BARE SOLE UPON HER BOSOM...

I SCREAM A CHALLENGE AND LAUNCH MY BODY, THIS ENGINE OF WAR, UPON MY FOE. HE TURNS AND SMILES, THE FIRES OF DISTANT WORLDS AND THE KNOWLEDGE OF THE EONS DANCE MOCKINGLY IN HIS EYES...

HE RELEASES HIS PRIZE, LIGHTING HER GENTLY ON THE DEWY SWARD...A SHAM, HIS GENTLENESS...A SIGN OF GALLANTRY FROM ONE SO GROSS IN SOUL AND FORM...HE MOCKS ME AND MY RAGE MOUNTS...

...WE MEET! A HEADLONG, BONE-CRUSHING COLLISION...FOR THE SCANTEST OF SECONDS, OUR FLESH AND SPIRITS SEEM TO MERGE. MY MIND IS LAID NUMB BY WHAT I FIND WITHIN THIS BLACK, POLLUTED HEART...FOR HERE IS A BEING EVIL INCARNATE...NO SPARK OF GOOD FLICKERS FEEBLY IN HIS BREAST...JUST TOTAL, SOUL SEARING EVIL!

...HE TAKES ADVANTAGE OF MY MOMEN-
TARY HORROR AND SHOCK, AND PUSHES
ME BACK...I FALL A HUNDRED MILES
AND STRIKE THE GROUND...MY ENTIRE
BEING IS STILLED, PARALYZED BY WHAT I
HAVE SEEN...

THREE TIMES BEFORE, I HAVE MET AND DESTROYED
MY UNNATURAL ENEMIES. THREE TIMES BEFORE, I
REGRETTED THE TAKING OF PHYSICAL LIFE, THE
SLAUGHTER OF LIVING THINGS...BUT NO MORE! I
FINALLY REALIZE THE TRUE MEANING OF MY TASK
...NOW, MY CAUSE! I HAVE BEEN SENT TO DESTROY
A SMALL PIECE OF HELL...AND IN THAT KNOW-
LEDGE, I FIND THE STRENGTH TO DO IT!

A BLURRED, SPEEDING TRUNCHEON DESCENDS UPON ME.
GATHERING MY WITS, I ROLL TO ONE SIDE AND CATCH THE
FALLING CLUB ON THE BLADE OF MY AXE...

...MY WEAPON IS USELESS,
ITS BLADE BURIED TOO DEEPLY
IN THE LOG TO REMOVE. I DON'T
KNOW WHAT TO DO...IT IS
REFLEX RATHER THAN STRAT-
EGY THAT GUIDES MY ARM
...I THROW THE RIDICULOUS
THING AT THE FACE OF MY
ATTACKER...HE GRINS,
AND COLD, DEAD LAUGHTER
ESCAPES HIS LIPS...

...HE MOVES, EASILY, AND
THE MISSLE STREAKS BY HIS
HEAD...BUT, THE FORCE
OF THE THROW PULLS ME
FORWARD AND THE HEAVY
CHAIN ENCIRCLES HIS
THROAT...I CATCH THE PRO-
JECTILE WITH THE SAME HAND
THAT LOOSED IT, AND HOLD
IT IN A GRIP THAT ONLY
DEATH WILL BREAK...

...THE OGRE GASPS
AND STRUGGLES BUT I
CLING TO HIM LIKE THE
WOLF TO THE BEAR...
THE SWEAT BEADS AND
ENCIRCLES MY BROW AND
THE OGRE SCREAMS...
HIS MOVEMENTS SLOW
AND FINALLY CEASE...
TILL HE DROWNS IN HIS
OWN BLOOD...

THE OGRE LIES STILL AT MY FEET AND I SEE HIM THROUGH COLD, REMORSELESS EYES. THEN, SOFTLY, THE GIRL APPROACHES . . . SHE TOUCHES MY SHOULDER, TREMBLING . . .

I TURN AND GAZE AT HER FACE, AND I GASP IN AWE. SHE IS, IN-DEED, THE MOST BEAUTIFUL CREATURE I'VE EVER SEEN. SHE SMILES AND HER EYES PROMISE FAVORS IN RETURN. I MOVE CLOSER . . .

OUR SOULS MEET AND WE GAZE UPON NEW WORLDS TOGETHER . . . UNIVERSES APPROACH, TOUCH AND PART AGAIN . . . WE LIE NAKED ON A GREEN, VELVET SWARD AND STARE DEEP INTO A VIBRANT, BLUE SKY . . .

. . . I AM BROUGHT BACK TO MY PURPOSE LIKE A DROWNING MAN PULLED TO SAFETY . . . I RISE, NOT WANTING TO LEAVE HER SIDE . . . MY WISH IS TO STAY WITH HER ALWAYS. I PROM-ISE TO RETURN AGAIN, WHEN MY TASK IS COM-PLETED . . . I KISS HER FARE-WELL AND TURN, WITHOUT A WORD, TO LEAVE . . .

. . . I AM NO MORE THAN TEN PACES AWAY, WHEN I FEEL THE MUSCLES AND TENDONS OF MY ARM BE-GIN TO STRAIN AND POP. I HALT, REFUSING TO ACCEPT THE FACT . . .

. . . I TURN, TRYING TO SMILE . . . SHE SMILES IN RE-TURN AND I SEE, FOR THE FIRST TIME, THE AGELESS EVIL MIRRORED IN THE DEPTHS OF HER EYES . . .

. . . FOR THE FIFTH TIME, MY FINGERS TIGHTEN ON THE HAFT OF MY BLADE . . . FOR THE FIFTH TIME ITS WORN EDGE MUST DRINK BLOOD . . . FOR THE FIRST TIME, A TEAR WELLS IN MY EYE . . . I AP-PROACH, SMILING THROUGH MISTY VISION. SOON, MY TASK WILL BE OVER . . .

THE END

MOST PEOPLE PLAY GAMES! SOME COME IN BOXES WITH BOARDS AND PIECES — A WORLD IN THEMSELVES OF CARDS AND DICE AND MARKERS! A SILENT CHALLENGE IS HURLED AT THE MIND OF THE PLAYER TO BE MET ON A CARDBOARD BATTLEFIELD!

MOST GAMES ARE PLAYED BY PEOPLE AGAINST PEOPLE! THIS IS THE TALE OF...

THE GAME THAT PLAYS YOU!

IT'S THE KIND OF STORE YOU WALK BY AND NEVER NOTICE. SNUGLY NESTLED BETWEEN TALL, ALIEN BUILDINGS, ITS VERY UNPRETENTIOUSNESS LENDS THE STORE AN AIR OF THE UNUSUAL...

S. STRANGE BOOKS
MAGIC · GAMES
OBJECTS OF OCCULT

THE WINDOW IS BLANKETED IN THE DUST OF DECADES. INSIDE LIE STACKS OF YELLOWED, FORGOTTEN VOLUMES TOGETHER WITH MEDIEVAL OBJECTS OF FEAR AND FASCINATION...

THE AROMA OF ANCIENT MAGIC STILL DWELLS WITHIN. ANTIQUITY REIGNS... EVERYTHING SUGGESTS THE PAST, THE DARK, DIM LONG AGO. THE STORE IS SILENT AS A TOMB UNTIL, FROM THE DARKNESS, A FORM APPEARS...

CAN I HELP YOU, SIR?

YES! I BELIEVE YOU CARRY YOUR OWN LINE OF ORIGINAL GAMES!

UNCOPYRIGHTED ORIGINAL GAMES! THIS GUY IS GOING TO MAKE ME RICH!

PERHAPS MY LATEST CREATION WOULD INTEREST YOU. IT'S THE MOST UNIQUE OF ALL! I CALL IT 'PREDESTINATION: THE GAME OF FATE'!

THE GAME INVENTOR'S EYES ARE BROODING — DARK WITH ANCIENT MYSTERIES...

I THINK YOU WILL FIND IT PARTICULARLY INTRIGUING! IT WILL INVOLVE YOU TO A DEGREE YOU'VE NEVER KNOWN BEFORE IN A GAME!

I SHOULD REMEMBER HIS PITCH! IT'LL COME IN HANDY WHEN I START PEDDLING THIS ONE TO THE COMPANIES!

YOU DON'T HAVE TO SELL ME ON YOUR GAMES! I BOUGHT A COPY OF YOUR LAST ONE!

I HAVE TO WARN YOU! YOU MUST PAY QUITE A PRICE FOR THIS ONE!

NONSENSE! IT'S WELL WORTH IT, WHATEVER THE COST!

VERY WELL, THEN! THIS ONE SELLS FOR FIFTY DOLLARS!

I'LL TAKE IT!

BUT, AS THE GAME THIEF LEAVES THE STORE IN TRIUMPH...

HE THINKS I HARBOR NO SUSPICIONS! I KNOW FULL WELL HE SOLD MY LAST GAME TO WILSON BROS. AS HIS OWN!

A YEAR AGO, I OFFERED IT TO THEM AND THEY REJECTED IT! BRILLIANTLY CONCEIVED BUT UNSALABLE, THEY SAID! MUCH TOO WEIRD!

NOW, IT SEEMS THE CLIMATE IS DIFFERENT! TIMES HAVE CHANGED! AND I AM SUPPOSED TO SUFFER FOR REFUSING TO CHANGE WITH THEM!

BUT, NO ONE CAN STEAL ONE OF MY GAMES AND GET AWAY WITH IT! NO ONE!

LITTLE DOES THE PAWN REALIZE THAT HE IS BUT A PIECE IN A MUCH LARGER GAME!

LIKE A CHILD WITH A NEW TOY, QUENTIN STERN, GAME THIEF, RUSHES TO HIS APARTMENT, HIS MIND SEETHING WITH CURIOSITY ABOUT THE PRIZE UNDER HIS ARM!

I HOPE THIS GAME IS AS GOOD AS ALL HIS OTHERS! IF IT IS, I'LL MAKE A FORTUNE WITH IT!

FEVERISH HANDS TREMBLE WITH ANTICIPATION AS HE TEARS THE WRAPPING PAPER TO REVEAL...

PREDEST A GAME OF FA

ALL HIS GAMES ARE A LITTLE WEIRD, BUT THAT'S WHAT SELLS TODAY! WHO AM I TO ARGUE WITH IT?

QUENTIN STERN PAUSES A MOMENT, SAVORING EACH SECOND OF EXPECTATION LIKE FINE WINE! LIFTING THE COVER, HE REMOVES THE GAME BOARD! A STRANGE GLOW EMANATES FROM ITS UNUSUALLY TEXTURED SURFACE, BATHING HIS FACE IN AN EERIE LIGHT!

I'VE NEVER SEEN ANYTHING LIKE THIS BOARD ...SUCH STRANGE DESIGNS! IT FEELS FLAT YET APPEARS TO HAVE DEPTH AND DIMENSION.

QUICKLY, HE ASSEMBLES THE PIECES IN FRONT OF HIM

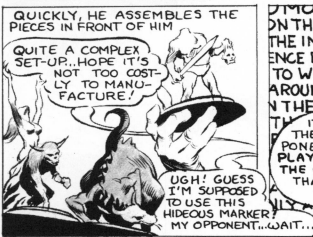

QUITE A COMPLEX SET-UP...HOPE IT'S NOT TOO COSTLY TO MANUFACTURE!

UGH! GUESS I'M SUPPOSED TO USE THIS HIDEOUS MARKER! MY OPPONENT...WAIT...

MOVE FROM ON THE OUTSIDE, THE INSIDE THEN ENCE BEFORE UND TO WHICH YOU P AROUND THE BOA N THE SAME PLAC

IT SAYS THERE'S NO OPPONENT! YOU PLAY AGAINST THE GAME! BUT THAT'S IMPOSSIBLE!

HOW CAN THE GAME PLAY AGAINST ME? IT HAS NO WILL OF ITS OWN!

THE MARKER IS PLACED ON THE START! THE FIRST CARD IS TURNED! QUENTIN'S HAND HESITATES! THE PIECE IS MOVED! THE WEIRD COLORS OF THE BOARD SPARKLE, SCINTILLATE, ENTICE HIS EYES! HIS HANDS REACH FOR THE DECKS! CARDS FLASH! FINGERS GRASP PRINTED INSTRUCTIONS! SEARCHING EYES RECEIVE THEIR ORDERS! THE MARKER ADVANCES!

THE BOARD IS ALIVE WITH COLOR AND LIGHT...SHINING, SHIMMERING, SWIRLING! THE SPACES CALL TO HIM, LURE HIM ON AND ON, DEEPER AND DEEPER, DOWN INTO THE SPINNING PINWHEEL DEPTHS OF THE GAME!

YOU CANNOT TAKE YOUR EYES OFF THE BOARD

BEGIN THE FINAL DESC

HIS VISION BLURS, HIS MIND REELS, REALITY RUNS FAR, FAR AWAY! HE FEELS HIMSELF FALLING THROUGH A VOID, TOWARD A BOTTOM THAT NEVER COMES! AND THEN IT STOPS... QUENTIN FEELS HIMSELF STANDING ON SOLID GROUND! HE WONDERS IF HE DARES OPEN HIS EYES! SLOWLY, FEARFULLY HIS EYELIDS OPEN TO REVEAL ... A NIGHTMARE WORLD, WHERE STRANGE CREATURES LEER FROM THE DARKNESS...

THIS ISN'T A GAME! IT'S A NIGHTMARE! NO! IT'S ALL...REAL!

BREATHING THE DANK AIR, HEAVY WITH EVIL, HE REALIZES...

I'M HOLDING THE SWORD, AND I'M ON THE GAME BOARD! BUT HOW DID I GET HERE? I CAN'T... THINK... ALL I REMEMBER IS THAT LAST CARD

WHAT IS THAT?

IF OUT IS WHERE YOU'D LIKE TO BE THE MAGIC NUMBER FOR YOU IS THREE!

THREE! I'D BETTER GO BACK TO THE START AND FIND THE SPACE!

THIS IS IT!

IT APPEARS I'M SUPPOSED TO STAND ON THIS STONE... ...WELL...

...HERE GOES!

THE SPACE BENEATH HIS FEET GIVES WAY! WITH A SICKENING LURCH, QUENTIN STERN DROPS INTO A PIT! UNABLE TO STOP HIMSELF, HE BEGINS A RIDE TOWARD MADNESS AND TERROR!

29

WAS IT ALL A DREAM? SUDDENLY, THE PAIN IS GONE, AND THERE IS ONLY A SWIRLING RED MIST...

HE'S GONE! AND THE BOARD IS GONE! WHERE AM I?

A FEELING OF DIZZYNESS SWEEPS OVER HIM, AS IF HIS MIND IS SLOWLY DRIFTING AWAY

EVERYTHING'S IN A CLOUD... I CAN'T SEE!

THERE! THE FOG IS LIFTING! THOSE FACES... COMING NEARER!

THE FACES APPROACH VERY SLOWLY, FOR IT IS SEVERAL HOURS BEFORE THE JANITOR NOTICES THE BLOOD SEEPING UNDER THE DOOR AND CALLS THE POLICE...

THAT'S HIM, ALRIGHT! GOOD LORD! WHAT A MESS!

GRUESOME! BETTER CALL THE MORGUE, JOE!

HE WAS NUTS ABOUT THESE WEIRD GAMES... GUESS MAYBE THAT'S WHAT FINALLY DROVE HIM CRAZY!

CRAZY? MAYBE SO... DOES LOOK LIKE SUICIDE!

PREDE

THOUGH, HOW HE MANAGED TO SLICE OFF HIS OWN HEAD WITH THIS OLD SWORD IS BEYOND ME!

WELL, QUENTIN ALWAYS DID WANT TO GET A-HEAD! NOW DON'T MISS MY NEXT THROBBING THRILLER

...FROM THE HALL, CAME A FAINT GURGLING SOUND...

TOM?!...

YOU WAIT THERE... I'LL BE RIGHT BACK.

CAUTIOUSLY, HE MAKES HIS WAY DOWN THE HALL, STRAINING HIS EYES IN THE DIRECTION OF THE NOISE.

HE REACHES THE HEAD OF THE STAIRS, WHERE HE SEES...

OH, MY GOD!!

HIS SCREAMS ARE UNHEARD, FROZEN IN HIS THROAT, AS THE GHOULISH HORDE ADVANCES UP THE STAIRCASE, GRAY CLODS OF GRAVE MUD AND ROTTED FLESH DROPPING IN ITS WAKE...

...CHOKED WITH HORROR AND GASPING IN DISGUST, HE BACKS AWAY, BUT TAKES ONLY TWO STEPS BEFORE BEING TRIPPED BY LONG BONY FINGERS...

...IN A MOMENT, THEY'RE ALL ABOUT HIM... PARALYZED WITH TERROR, HE CAN DO NOTHING BUT WATCH AS THEY PULL AND CLUTCH, SLOWLY SUBDUING HIM BY STRENGTH OF NUMBERS... COLD BLACK CLAWS SINK INTO HIS FLESH...

...SUDDENLY, HIS HORROR LEAVES HIM, REPLACED BY RAGE AND ANGER, ENABLING HIM TO FIGHT BACK!

THE FIGHTING BRINGS THEM CLOSE TO THE STAIR-HEAD. WITH A DESPERATE KICK, HE SENDS ONE OF THEM INTO THE PUTRESCENT CROWD ON THE STAIRS, MOMENTARILY SLOWING THEM.

...HEAD REELING, HE STAGGERS QUICKLY DOWN THE HALL, BACK TO ANNIE'S ROOM...

...ONCE INSIDE, HE SLAMS THE DOOR AND LEANS AGAINST IT, COLD SWEAT BEADING HIS BROW...

THOSE...THINGS OUT THERE... HORRIBLE... WHAT DO THEY WANT OF ME?...

YOU DON'T KNOW?... ...I'LL TELL YOU...

HE STARES AT HER, INCREDULOUSLY

WHAT?!... YOU... YOU KNOW ABOUT THEM?... I...

YOU DIDN'T LET ME FINISH MY STORY. AS I WAS SAYING...

...I WAS READY TO BE MARRIED. THE CEREMONIES, INCLUDING THE RE-CEPTION, WERE HELD IN THIS VERY HOUSE.

THOUGH NOT INVITED, YOU WERE THERE, THE JEALOUSY IN YOU DEMANDING BUT ONE THING... REVENGE ...REVENGE ON THOSE MORE FORTUNATE THAN YOU...

"WHILE THE PARTY WAS IN PROGRESS, YOU SPIKED THE PUNCH, USING ENOUGH ARSENIC TO POISON HALF THE CITY..."

...AS A RESULT, EVERYONE THERE DIED... ...HORRIBLY.

BUT... I ... ...I DON'T...

OUTSIDE THE ROOM, HE COULD HEAR THEM LURCHING AND STUMBLING... PAINFULLY MAKING THEIR WAY DOWN THE HALL...

YOU DON'T REMEMBER? OF COURSE NOT!... YOUR DEED WAS SO WRETCHED, SO HORRIBLE, THAT YOU BLOCKED IT FROM YOUR MIND, REFUSED TO ACCEPT IT... INDUCED A STATE OF SELF-AMNESIA SO YOUR CONSCIENCE WOULDN'T DRIVE YOU MAD!!...

THEY WERE RIGHT OUTSIDE, NOW... HE COULD HEAR THEM POUNDING FEEBLY ON THE DOOR...

THEN... THEY... OUT THERE... GOOD LORD!!

YES... THE PEOPLE YOU MURDERED MORE THAN TEN YEARS AGO.

...IT ALL BEGAN TO COME BACK NOW — THE HAPPY WEDDING GUESTS... ...THE SMALL BLUE VIAL OF ARSENIC TWO HUNDRED FIFTY CORPSES...

...ALREADY, THE DOOR BEGINS TO BUCKLE BENEATH THE MASSIVE WEIGHT OF THE ONSLAUGHT...

C'MON, ANNIE... LET'S GET OUTTA HERE WHILE THERE'S STILL TIME!

ALRIGHT, TOM...

...YOU KNOW, TOM... TEN YEARS AGO YOU COULD'NT HAVE ME... BUT NOW, I'M ALL YOURS.

JUST THEN, THE DOOR GAVE WAY.

THE LEGEND OF SLEEPY HOLLOW

ABOUT TWO MILES FROM TARRY TOWN, THERE IS A LITTLE VALLEY AMONG HIGH HILLS, WHICH IS ONE OF THE QUIETEST PLACES IN THE WHOLE WORLD...

...A DROWSY, DREARY INFLUENCE SEEMS TO HANG OVER THE LAND AND TO PERVADE ITS VERY ATMOSPHERE. IT HAS BECOME KNOWN AS SLEEPY HOLLOW.

THERE CAME TO THIS PLACE A LIVING SCARECROW OF A SCHOOLMASTER NAMED ICHABOD CRANE.

ADAPTED FROM WASHINGTON IRVING'S SHORT STORY BY VIRGIL NORTH
ILLUSTRATED BY JEFF JONES ALAN WEISS BERNI WRIGHTSON
© 1970

AFTER SCHOOL HOURS, ICHABOD MADE A SMOOTH TRANSITION TO THE NON-ACADEMIC FACETS OF HIS POSITION. HIS SEVERITY GONE, HE BECAME A READY COMPANION TO THOSE BOYS WHO HAPPENED TO HAVE PRETTY SISTERS! IF THE MOTHER OF ONE OF HIS STUDENTS WAS KNOWN FOR KEEPING A GOOD CUPBOARD, ICHABOD WOULD OFTEN WALK THE BOY HOME. THE WOMEN WERE PLEASED WITH HIS PRESENCE AND HIS PLENTIFUL GOSSIP!

CRANE WAS IDEALLY SUITED FOR THE ONE ROOM SCHOOLHOUSE, BEING EDUCATED IN ALL AREAS OF ACADEMICS AS WELL AS DISCIPLINE! AWARE OF THE NONCHALANT ATTITUDE OF HIS PUPIL'S PARENTS TOWARD BOOK LEARNING, HE PURSUED HIS DUTIES WITH THE UTMOST FERVOR. HE BELIEVED HIMSELF TO BE A KIND AND CONSCIENTIOUS MAN, BUT WAS QUICK TO ADMINISTER THE BIRCH ROD TO A LAZY SCHOLAR!

ONE OF HIS CHIEF SOURCES OF PLEASURE WAS PASSING THE LONG WINTER NIGHTS WITH THE OLD DUTCH WIVES AS THEY SAT SPINNING BY THE FIRE, MANY A CHILLING STORY THEY WOVE, AND NONE WAS TOO MONSTROUS OR TERRIFYING FOR HIS TASTES. HERE HE LEARNED THE HISTORY AND LORE OF THE AREA, OF GHOSTS, GOBLINS, AND THE **HEADLESS HORSEMAN!**

THE HORSEMAN IS SAID TO BE A HESSIAN TROOPER WHOSE HEAD WAS TORN FROM HIS BODY BY A STRAY CANNONBALL DURING A FORGOTTEN BATTLE OF THE REVOLUTION

ICHABOD'S MIND, REARED ON SUPERSTITION, WAS FILLED WITH TREPIDATION AS HE WALKED HOME FROM THESE SESSIONS.

ASIDE FROM THE OTHER FACETS OF HIS POSITION, HE MOST ENJOYED HIS SOCIAL LIFE. AMONG THE YOUNG LADIES OF HIS AQUAINTANCE WAS KATRINA VAN TASSEL, THE DAUGHTER OF A SUBSTANTIAL DUTCH FARMER. SHE, (AND HER FATHER'S ESTATE), CAUGHT ICHABOD'S FANCY, AND HE SOUGHT TO WIN HER FAVOR.

HE WAS NOT ALONE IN HIS QUEST FOR KATRINA'S ATTENTION. ONE BROM VAN BRUNT WATCHED THESE ANTICS WITH AMUSEMENT.

VAN BRUNT WAS A MOUNTAIN OF A GOOD NATURED ROGUE, AND THE HERO OF THE COUNTRY ROUND. A MATCH BETWEEN THE TWO SUITORS WOULD HAVE BEEN UNSPORT-ING, SO HE CONTENTED HIMSELF WITH HARMLESS PRANKS AND SMALL HUMILIATIONS. ICHABOD HAD NO MEANS OF RETALIATION, AND WENT HIS WAY APPARENTLY OBLIVIOUS TO THE HURT.

ONE TEDIOUS AUTUMN DAY, ICHABOD WAS APPROACHED WITH AN INVITATION TO A QUILTING FROLIC. THE BEARER OF THE MES-SAGE WAS A SERVANT OF THE VAN TASSELS. THE SCHOOLMASTER WAS ELATED AT THE PROSPECT OF ALL THE FOOD HE COULD EAT, A CHANCE TO DISPLAY HIS DANCING ABILITY, ... AND A CHANCE TO SEE KATRINA AGAIN!

DISMISSING HIS STUDENTS EARLY, DONNING HIS BEST HAT AND MOUNTING HIS FIERY STEED, GUNPOWDER, ICHABOD SET OUT FOR THE VAN TASSEL ESTATE.

THE HORSE, A BORROWED MOUNT A BIT PAST IT'S PRIME, CONSIDERED WALKING A BREAKNECK SPEED!

WHEN HE FINALLY ARRIVED AT THE PARTY, HE WAS GREETED ENTHUSIASTICALLY BY THE OTHER GUESTS, BUT HAD EYES ONLY FOR THE FEAST ON THE HEAVILY LADEN HAR- -VEST TABLE IT WAS A RARE CHANCE FOR HIM TO EAT HIS FILL, AND HE INDULGED HIMSELF AS NEVER BEFORE.

THE FOOD WHETTED HIS APPETITE FOR DANCING, AND HE WAS AMAZING TO BEHOLD. SECURE IN HIS DANCING ABILITY, HE CHOSE TO IGNORE THE GLOWERING EYES OF VAN BRUNT.

WHEN THE EVENING WAS OVER AND THE GUESTS HAD DEPARTED, ICHABOD REMAINED BEHIND TO SPEAK TO KATRINA. NO ONE KNOWS THE SUBJECT OF THEIR CONVERSATION, BUT IT WAS A DOWNHEARTED FIGURE THAT WAS SEEN LEAVING THE ESTATE SOMETIME AFTERWARD.

HE STARTED DEJECTEDLY HOMEWARD AS THE WITCHING HOUR APPROACHED. SLOWLY HE BECAME AWARE OF A GHOSTLY FIGURE IN THE DISTANCE. HE WAS IN THE REPUTEDLY HAUNTED AREA, AND HIS HEART THUMPED WILDLY AS HE NEARED THE SHADOWY HORSEMAN.

SUDDENLY THE HORSE REARED AND IT'S RIDER WAS SILHOUETTED AGAINST THE MOON. ICHABOD REALIZED IN HORROR THAT THIS WAS NO MORTAL RIDER THAT STALKED HIM... ...... FOR THE FIGURE HAD NO HEAD!

HIS HORROR WAS STILL MORE INCREASED ON OBSERVING THAT THE HEAD, WHICH SHOULD HAVE RESTED ON HIS SHOULDERS, WAS CARRIED BEFORE HIM ON THE POMMEL OF HIS SADDLE.

FRANTICALLY SPURRING HIS TERRIFIED MOUNT, ICHABOD SOUGHT TO AVOID THE TERRIBLE APPARITION.

NOW THEY HAD REACHED THE ROAD THAT TURNS OFF TO SLEEPY HOLLOW. IN THIS GRIM RACE, THANKS TO AN IMPROBABLE QUIRK OF FATE COUPLED WITH ICHABOD'S DESPERATION, GUNPOWPER WAS IN THE LEAD BY A LENGTH. ICHABOD SOUGHT TO REACH THE CHURCH BRIDGE, WHERE, ACCORDING TO LEGEND, THE PHANTOM MUST DISAPPEAR.

THE SADDLE WAS SLIPPING PRECARIOUSLY AND GUNPOWDER'S STAMINA WAS FAST GIVING WAY AS THEY APPROACHED THEIR GOAL. ICHABOD LOOKED BACK HOPING TO SEE THE SPECTRAL DUO VANISH AS THEY SHOULD HAVE.

JUST THEN HE SAW THE GOBLIN RISE UP IN HIS SADDLE, IN THE VERY ACT OF HURLING HIS HEAD!

49

ICHABOD ENDEAVORED TO DODGE THE HORRIBLE MISSILE, BUT TOO LATE! IT ENCOUNTED THE BACK OF HIS HEAD WITH A TREMENDOUS SPLATTER. HE WAS A WINDMILL OF SPIDERY ARMS AND LEGS AS HE WENT CAREENING INTO THE DUST!

GUNPOWDER, THE GOBLIN RIDER, AND THE BLACK STEED PASSED BY LIKE A WHIRLWIND!

THE WAS MUCH SPECULATION ON WHAT HAD BECOME OF ICHABOD. THE OLD WIVES INSISTED THAT HE HAD BEEN CARRIED OFF BY THE HEADLESS HORSEMAN, AND A TRAVELLING MAN SWORE HE HAD SEEN A MAN OF THAT DESCRIPTION A JUDGE IN A FAR AWAY TOWN.

THE MORNING AFTER THE FATEFUL RIDE, THE ONLY EVIDENCE OF WHAT HAD HAPPENED WAS THE UNSADDLED GUNPOWDER, A SHATTERRED PUMPKIN, AND BESIDE THESE, THE PECULIAR HAT OF ICHABOD CRANE. HOWEVER, IN YEARS AFTERWARD, MENTION OF THE INCIDENT WAS SURE TO BRING UNCONTROLLED LAUGHTER FROM ONE BROM VAN BRUNT!

— The End —

THOK
THOK THOK
THOK
THOK THOK
THOK
THOK THOK
THOK

IS THE KID ASLEEP YET? *NEVER MIND ABOUT THE KID — TELL ME WHERE YOU'VE BEEN ALL DAY!!* I DON'T THINK IT'S ANY OF YOUR DAMN BUSINESS WHERE I'VE BEEN!! *OH, ZATSO?!* YEAH!! *SHUT UP, YOU WORTHLESS, STUPID BUM — YOU'LL WAKE BILLY!!* SO WHAT?!! *STUPID, HUH?! WELL, LEMME TELL YOU SOME-THING...* I DON'T WANNA HEAR IT... *YOU'LL HEAR IT ALRIGHT... CLOSE THE DOOR!* YOU'RE GONNA WAKE BILLY!! *SO, I'LL WAKE BILLY!!* YOU'RE NOT EXACTLY WHISPERIN', YOURSELF, Y'KNOW... *YOU'RE CALLING ME A LOUDMOUTH?!* YEAH!

WRIGHTSON '71

WELL, HELLO, BILLY! IT'S BEEN A LONG TIME SINCE YOU WERE HERE LAST... IT'S GOOD TO SEE YOU AGAIN...MMM ...YOU SEEM TO HAVE GROWN A LITTLE...OR MAYBE IT'S SOMETHING OTHER THAN TIME THAT'S OLDENED YOUR FACE.

COME ALONG, MY YOUNG FRIEND. I'M GOING TO SHOW YOU SOME THINGS YOU HAVEN'T SEEN BEFORE...PERHAPS YOU WON'T UNDERSTAND IT ALL...AH, BUT OF COURSE YOU WILL. YOU'RE STILL A BRIGHT ONE AND THERE'S MUCH OF LIFE TO LEARN HERE...

58

DO YOU SEE THAT CASTLE BEYOND THE WOOD? IT LOOKS QUITE STRONG AND STATELY, DOESN'T IT? IT'S A SHAM, BILLY, IT IS MADE OF SAND AND SHELLS, AND WILL CRUMBLE AT THE TOUCH OF YOUR HAND. . . NOTHING LASTS.

. . . AND THOSE CREATURES THERE . . . THEY'RE *GIFTERS*, THEY'LL LET YOU HAVE ANYTHING YOU WANT. . . PROVIDED ITS BADNESS IS COVERED WITH CINNAMON PAINT. . . SOUR SWEETS, TAINTED FRUIT, SHARP LITTLE THINGS TO STICK IN THE GROUND . . .

. . .AND THOSE ARE THE CHANGLINGS. . .
FOUL, TERRIBLE, GRAVE-WORM PEOPLE
LURKING WITHIN BEAUTIFUL,
INNOCENT SHELLS. . .

SO, YOU SEE, BILLY. . .MANY THINGS ARE
NOT WHAT THEY SEEM. . .TOO
MUCH OF LOTS OF STUFF IS SUGAR-AND-
SPICE COATED MAGGOTS. . .YOU MUST
LEARN WARINESS AND DISCRE-
TION. . .IN EVERYTHING.

BUT, COME NOW. FOLLOW ME.
THERE IS BUT ONE MORE TO SEE . . .

THERE IS *THE REAPER OF LOVE!* BEWARE HIM THE MOST FOR HE IS THE *FATHER OF PAIN* . . . HE EATS BROKEN HEARTS AND DRINKS SHED TEARS!

HIS FACES AND FORMS ARE MANY . . . HE LURKS INSIDE THOSE WE KNOW . . . KILLING US DAY BY DAY, LITTLE BY LITTLE . . . HE MANGLES OUR GUTS, ROTTING US FROM THE INSIDE OUT . . .

. . . BILLY . . . ?

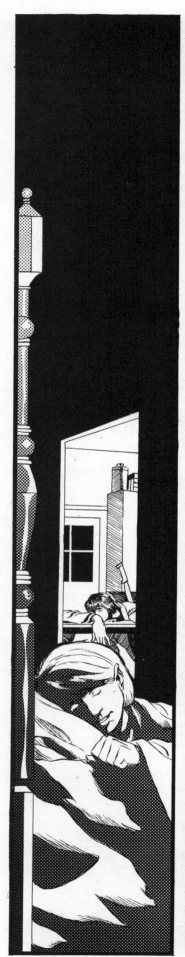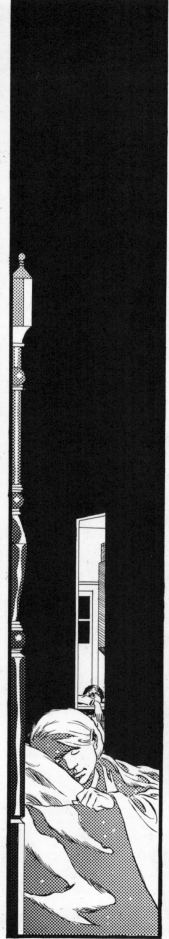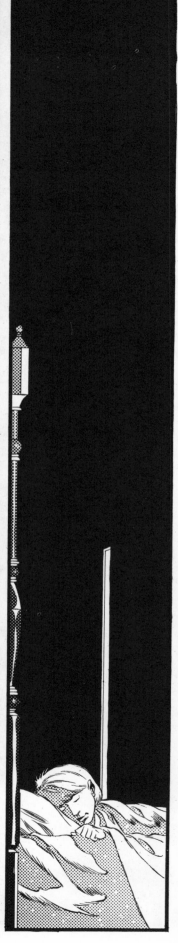

OUT ON A LIMB!

I WAS BORN WITH THREE ARMS. ALL MY LIFE, I'VE BEEN A FREAK...

...TODAY, I AM A MURDERER...

...I CAME INTO TOWN EARLY THIS MORNING...

...HE STARTED IN RIGHT AWAY. A NEW FACE, OF COURSE...

HEY, YOU'RE NEW HERE, RIGHT? HOW 'BOUT BUYIN' GOOD OL' TOM WILLIS A DRINK?

...BUT ALWAYS THE SAME PERSON.

C'MON, BOY! WHAT-SAMATTER? CAN'T-CHA TALK?

HEYYYYY!

LET GO!!

SOMEONE ALWAYS STARTS TROUBLE... AND TOM WILLIS KEPT THE PATTERN CONSISTENT...

MY GOD!! LOOK AT HIM!

TH-THREE ARMS!!

BOY, YOU JUST MADE A BIG MIS-TAKE...

WHY CAN'T PEOPLE TAKE TIME TO UNDERSTAND? WHY MUST THEY ALWAYS JUMP TO CONCLUSIONS, STRIKING OUT TO DESTROY THINGS BEYOND THEIR COMPREHENSION?

THE LAST GUY THAT SHOVED TOM WILLIS AROUND SPENT TWO MONTHS IN A BED AFTERWARDS...

HAH! YOU MOVE RIGHT QUICK... CONSIDERIN' YOU GOT AN EXTRA ARM TO SLOW YOU DOWN...

ALL MY LIFE, I'VE SEEN IT IN THEIR EYES... THE MINGLING OF FEAR AND HATE...

I SWEAR...YOU LOOK JUST LIKE A TREE STANDIN' THERE – WHAT WITH ALL YER LIMBS. C'MON, BOY, I'M GONNA SHOW YOU WHAT HAPPENS TO FREAKS AROUND HERE...

I'VE NEVER ENCOUNTERED A SINGLE WORD OF KINDNESS... NEVER A FRIENDLY SMILE... ONLY LOOKS OF HORROR AND DISGUST, FEAR, SUSPICION...

...THERE HAD TO BE A BREAKING POINT... I COULDN'T MERELY DEFEAT HIM...

I COULDN'T GIVE HIM A BEATING AND JUST WALK AWAY, KNOWING I'D MEET ANOTHER TOM WILLIS, IN ANOTHER TOWN, ANOTHER DAY...

... I HAD TO AVENGE MYSELF, NOT ONLY ON THIS TOM WILLIS, BUT ALL THE OTHERS PAST... I HAD TO PIERCE HIS HEART AND SOUL TO EASE THE WOUNDS IN MINE...

AS I LOOKED DOWN ON THE RESULTS OF MY DEED, I FELT A STRANGE SENSE OF FULFILMENT AND SAT-ISFACTION, NEVER BEFORE EXPERIENCED...

...AS IF IN KILLING TOM WILLIS, I HAD DESTROYED THE CONSUMMATE IN EVIL AND PREJUDICE...

FILTHY MURDERIN' FREAK!

SOMEBODY GRAB 'IM!

STOP HIM — HE'S GETTING AWAY!!

HEY, YOU— OOF!!

...AND NOW, THERE'S NO ESCAPING MY FATE... EVEN THOUGH I RUN I KNOW I'LL SOON HAVE TO STAND AND PAY FOR MY CRIME...

...FOR WHEN THEY REACH ME — MY GANG OF SELF-APPOINTED EXECUTIONERS — I'LL NOT RESIST...

I'LL TAKE MY PUNISHMENT LIKE THE MAN THEY THINK I'M *NOT* — BUT, THEIR PURPOSE ISN'T ONLY TO PUNISH A MUR-DERER...

...I MUST DIE BECAUSE I'M A FREAK ...BECAUSE I WAS BORN WITH *'ONE TOO MANY'*...

...I GUESS THERE'S JUST NO ROOM IN THE WORLD FOR FREAKS...

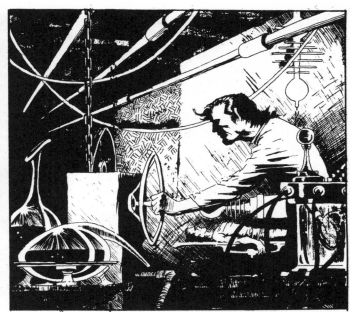
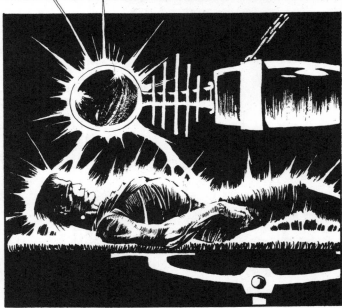

BOIIINNNG!!...HIYA, KIDS, HIYA, HIYA, HIYA... THIS IS YOUR HOR-RENDOUS HOST IN HEATHER HOPPIN' HORROR, THE GREMLIN FROG... FRESH-CRAWLED FROM MY BED OF BILEOUS BARF-SLIME TO BEND YOUR EAR WITH A BONE-BREAKING BIT OF BAD BEDLAM. SO, PULL UP THAT POT OF PUTRESCENT PIG-PARTS WHILST I DESTROY YOUR MIND WITH THIS LITTLE PORTION OF PUCE CALLED...

CONJURE WOMAN

THE OLD WOMAN, STIRRING HER STEAMING CAULDRON WITH ALL THE CARE OF A MIDWIFE, COUGHED AND CHUCKLED AMIDST HER TOMES AND BOTTLES AND JARS, THEIR DARK TREASURES LOOKING ON APPROVINGLY... THE MYSTERIOUS CONTENTS OF HER GLOWING KETTLE POPPED AND BUBBLED, SWIRLED ABOUT IN EVER-CHANGING PATTERNS, AND THE GREASY BLACK FUMES ESCAPED THROUGH A HOLE IN THE ROOF OF HER ANCIENT HOVEL, STAINING THE DANK SWAMP AIR WITH THEIR OBSCENE COLOR...

MAUDLIN Love COMIX

LUCY LIPSHITZ SAT, EVERYDAY, IN FRONT OF 'BOR-TCHTEL'S BETTER BUTCHER SHOP' PLAYING HEART RENDING TUNES ON HER HONER, COLLECTING ANY SMALL CHANGE THAT RATTLED INTO THE TIN CUP HANGING BETWEEN HER BREASTS. LUCY WAS A QUADRAPLEGIC, THROUGH AN UNFORTUNATE ACCIDENT OF BIRTH,... AN ARMLESS AND LEGLESS TORSO...

...DAY AFTER DAY, SHE SAT, WATCHING AS THE YOUNG LOVERS STROLLED BY, ARMS INTERTWINED, LAUGHING AND TALKING AS LOVERS HAVE ALWAYS AND WILL ALWAYS DO...

SHE SAT AND SHE WATCHED, PLAYING 'IT'S TH' SYMETH' 'OLE WORL' OVEH' ON HER HARMONICA HOPING TO LURE SOMEONE INTO A CONVERSATION, HOP-ING ONLY FOR A KIND WORD,... A SMILE...

SHE KNEW SHE WAS RE-PULSIVE,... AND SHE KNEW IT WASN'T HER FAULT,...WAS SHE DOOMED BY A FREAK OF NATURE TO SPEND HER LIFE AND NEVER KNOW LOVE? LUCY THOUGHT, AND SHE CRIED...

LUCY WASN'T UNATTRACTIVE...SHE KNEW. HER FACE HELD A KIND OF SORROWFUL BEAUTY THAT WAS ALL HER OWN...HER FIGURE WAS STRONG AND SULTRY,... IT WAS HER ABSENCE OF LIMBS THAT DE-PRIVED HER THE JOY THAT OTHERS KNEW...

...AND, THEN, IT HAPPENED... SEEMINGLY OUT OF NOWHERE, HE CAME AND BLUNDERED INTO HER. 'HOW COULD ANYONE BE SO CLUMSY', THOUGHT LUCY...

...AND THEN SHE SAW HIM,...SPRAWL-ED ON THE SIDEWALK... HIS THIGHS ENDING IN STUMPS. HE RAISED HIM-SELF UP AND PROMPTLY POURED FORTH APOLOGIES AND EXPLANA-TIONS... HE RAISED HER TO HER FORMER SITTING POSITION, THEN CHANCED TO LOOK INTO HER EYES... ...WHO KNOWS WHAT MAGIC WORKED IN THEIR HEARTS AS HE CLIMBED ONTO HIS WHEEL-BOARD,... HE ASKED FOR A DATE ...AND LUCY SAID YES...

...HIS NAME WAS MORDIQUEY WRENCH, AND AS HE AND LUCY TALKED IN HIS APARTMENT, SHE FOUND HIM VERY MUCH LIKE HERSELF,...AND AS THE EVENING WORE ON, SHE FELL IN LOVE... BUT, COULD THEY MAKE IT WORK? THEY COULD TRY...

...AND THEY TRIED,...AND THEY WERE BEAUTIFUL! IT WASN'T LONG AFTER THAT THEY WERE MARRIED AT A QUIET CEREMONY IN THE CHURCH OF THEIR CHOICE....

..., AND SO, TO CORN A PHRASE, THEY LIVED HAP-PILY EVERAFTER. MORDIQUEY BUILT A LARGE WHEEL-BOARD WITH A ROLL-BAR ON THE BACK FOR LUCY, AND THEY WORKED TOGETHER... MORDI-QUEY SANG AND LUCY ACCOMPANIED HIM ON HER HONER. THE BIG WHEEL-BOARD MADE THINGS ROUGH IN THE SUBWAY, BUT THEY MANAGED... ...THEY MANAGED VERY WELL ...

NOSFERATU

BREMEN, GERMANY, OCT. 2, 19—
GUSTAV HUNTER, REAL ESTATE AGENT, PREPARED FOR A DISTANT TRIP.

GUSTAV, PLEASE BE CAREFUL... I'VE HEARD TALES OF THAT COUNTRY...

ELLEN, MY SWEET... THEY'RE MERELY CHILDHOOD FANTASIES...

PERHAPS! BUT THE SECRETIVE INNER WORLD OF THE CARPATHIAN MOUNTAINS HAS SEEN STRANGE THINGS ESCAPE ITS FOG-SHROUDED BORDERS.

TRANSYLVANIA, OCT. 11, 19—
A JOURNEY OF FIRST SHIP, THEN TRAIN, NOW SPECTRAL COACH, WINDS ITS WAY PAST THE LAST TRACES OF MODERNITY INTO A LAND WHERE TIME IS SEEMINGLY TRAPPED SOMEWHERE IN THE MIDDLE AGES. PEASANTS DRESSED OF YEARS PAST HAD INCANTED OMINOUS SLAVIC GUTTURALS LADEN WITH DEMONIC IMPLICATIONS.

THE MOUNTAINOUS ASCENT THROUGH ROCK-STREWN PATHS WAS AIDED BY A BRIGHT, LEPROUS ORANGE MOON STRUNG ABOVE THE BLACK AND GRAY LANDSCAPE. THERE WAS NO DISCERNABLE LIFE SAVE THE FLEETING SHADOWS OF BEASTS AND BATS AND MOUNTAIN RODENTIA. SOON, THE CASTLE LOOMED CLOSE AND BEFORE THE MASSIVE DOORS, THE HOST...

COUNT ORLOCK

AH! WELCOME, MR. HUNTER! YOU MAY REST NOW FROM YOUR TRIP. WE'LL DISCUSS BUSINESS LATER!

SLEEP INDEED, POOR GUSTAV, WHILE A SERPENTINE FIGURE CRAWLS TO YOUR BEDSIDE, SEEKING TO DEPRIVE YOU OF YOUR LIFE'S SOURCE AND GIVE YOU ETERNAL REST, BUT SOMEWHERE ABOVE THE SEPARATION OF MANY MILES, A BATTLE OF DARK AND LIGHT IS WAGED AND WON...
...BY A WHISPER...

GUSTAV...
...GUSTAV...

THE POWER OF LOVE PIERCES TIME AND SPACE...

...DEALING THE HUMAN REPTILE A STABBING BLOW OF GOODNESS...

...THE NEFARIOUS NOSFERATU LEAVES HIS NEAR VICTIM BEHIND AND BOARDS A SHIP BOUND FOR BREMEN, THERE TO FIND NEW BLOOD FOR HIS INQUENCHABLE THIRST. EVIL INCARNATE, SCULPTED BY THE DEVIL'S OWN HAND, THIS MONSTER WILL NOT BE STILL AS LONG AS FEAR IS HIS WEAPON...

HAVING GATHERED BACK HIS WITS AND RESOURCES, GUSTAV HUNTER ESCAPED THE WEB OF CASTLE ORLOCK. THINKING HE HAD ESCAPED THE VAMPIRE AS WELL, HE RODE TO BEAT THE WIND AND HURRIED HOME TO BREMEN, AND ELLEN.

OCT. 19, 19— NOSFERATU ARRIVES AT BREMEN AND BRINGS WITH HIM ON THE BACKS OF HIS RATS AN ARMY MORE DEVASTATING THAN ANY MADE OF MEN, THE RODENT MESSENGERS SILENTLY SCURRY OFF TO ALL THE CITY'S CRACKS AND CORNERS. THEY DRINK THE TOWN'S WATER AND EAT ITS FOOD, AND AS THEY DO, LET ROLL OFF THEIR SIDES AN INVISIBLE HORDE OF GERMS.....THE KIND THAT CAUSES...

A HAGGARD AND WEARY HUNTER HAS RETURNED TO BREMEN TO FIND HIMSELF AMIDST A RAVAGING SICKNESS, HE RECOUNTS TO ELLEN HIS TERRIBLE DAYS AT CASTLE ORLOCK. THEY SOON REALIZE THE HORRIBLE TRUTH, THAT NOSFERATU MUST BE THE PLAGUE'S CAUSE...

AND LEAVES A WHOLE POPULACE WEAK AGAINST THE MIDNIGHT VISITS OF THE VAMPIRE...

...UNKNOWN TO HER HUSBAND, ELLEN HAS FORMULATED A DARING, AND VERY DANGEROUS PLAN. SHE INFORMS ORLOCK, BY, NOTE, THAT SHE'S AWARE OF HIM AND INVITES HIM TO PAY HER A NIGHT CALL...

THE PESTILENT PROVACATUER ENTERS AS EXPECTED WITH ARMS LOOMING CLAW-LIKE OVER THE YOUNG FEMALE. SHE, WITHOUT FEAR, AND HANDS BECKONING, WELCOMES THE HIDEOUS NIGHT-CRAWLER. THIS DISMAYS THE ADVANCING ORLOCK, FOR FRIGHT MAKES HIS MENACE WORK. HE HESITATES, CAUGHT IN A SPELL OF CONFUSION. HIS BEWILDERMENT FINDS THE MINUTES PASSING AND THE VAMPIRE UNAWARE THAT...

...THE WEAPON OF FEAR IS FOR ONCE AND ALWAYS DEFEATED BY THE HEART OF A STRONG AND GOOD WOMAN.

...AS MYSTERIOUSLY AS IT APPEARED, THE PLAGUE VANISHED, FREEING BREMEN FROM THE CHAINS OF EVIL, AND OUTSIDE A HOUSE, NEIGHBORS WONDER WHY A CERTAIN WINDOW IS BEING BOARDED, NEVER REALIZING THAT THEIR FREEDOM DEPENDS ON THE PERPETUAL ENCLOSURE INTO OBLIVION OF THE THING CALLED...

NOSFERATU

GHASTLY HORROR COMIX

I- I THINK I'M GOIN' TO BE SICK!

ZARKLEY NITCHWITT FELT SATISFIED INDEED AS HE STRETCHED OUT IN HIS SUMPTUOUS BED, READY TO READ HIMSELF TO SLEEP... ZARKLEY NITCHWITT WAS A MURDERER...

IT WAS NOW A YEAR SINCE HIS FORMER PARTNER, THORNTON TARR, HAD BEEN INTERRED IN HIS PLOT IN 'HILLTOP GARDENS', FOLLOWING THE DISCOVERY OF HIS DROWNED AND BLOATED CORPSE...

...HE SMILED AS HE REMEMBERED THORNTON'S THRASHING, KICKING STRUGGLES AS ZARKLEY SHOVED HIS HEAD DEEP INTO THE TOILET... HE COULD NOT HEAR THE WHISPERINGS AND STIRRINGS IN THE CEMETERY ABOVE THE TOWN...

HOW EASY IT HAD BEEN TO THROW THORNTON'S ALREADY DEAD BODY INTO THE CESS-POOL... ZARKLEY COULD NOT HEAR THE FAINTLY MUTTERED OATHS AND CURSES... THE SCRATCHING SOUNDS...

...HE COULD NOT SEE THE ROTTED, FETID, CLAW-LIKE, SKELETAL HANDS BREAK THE MOULDY CRUST AND GROPE AT THE BRISK, AUTUMN AIR...

...HOW COULD HE KNOW THAT THORNTON TARR HAD RETURNED WITH VENGEANCE IN THE DECAYING, DRIPPING THING THAT WAS ONCE HIS HEART...
...IT WAS FREE NOW... FREE FROM THE EARTHEN PRISON WHICH HAD HELD IT FOR SO LONG... BITS OF PUTRESCENT, LIQUEFIED FLESH OOZED AND DRIPPED FROM ITS SWAYING, TEETERING FORM...

IT MOVED OUT OF ITS PLOT, LEAVING A WINDING TRAIL OF CLODS OF SLIMY, WORM-RIDDEN MUD AND POOLS OF FOUL, REEKING, ROTTING MUSCLE AND TISSUE AS IT MADE ITS WAY THROUGH THE LEANING, TILTING TOMBSTONES...

...THROUGH THE WROUGHT-IRON GATES AND INTO THE TINY, TWISTING, NARROW STREETS OF THE VILLAGE...

...IT KNEW WHERE IT WAS GOING... TOTTERED DRUNKENLY TO ITS DESTINATION... LEAVING A PUTRID WAKE OF FEOTOR FROM THE LOOSENED, SCALY FLESH...

...IT FOUND ITS WAY TO ZARKLEY'S HOUSE... STOOD STARING AT THE LIGHTED WINDOW... THEN STAGGERING UP THE PORCH STEPS... THE FATEFUL MOMENT WAS AT HAND — THORNTON HAD WAITED A LONG TIME FOR REVENGE... AND HE KNEW WHAT HE WAS TO DO...

NITCHWITT TARR INSURANCE

...IT BEGAN TO HAMMER ON THE BROAD, OAKEN DOOR WITH ROTTING, BLISTERED FISTS, THE FINGERNAILS AND KNUCKLES FALLING AWAY MORE AND MORE WITH EACH RESOUNDING BLOW...

THE THUNDEROUS SLAMS VIBRATED THE WALLS OF THE OLD HOUSE, SENDING ZARKLEY NITCHWITT INTO A FIT OF COLD HORROR. HE KNEW, OR RATHER SENSED THE PRESENCE OF IMPENDING TERROR...

HE GRABBED A PISTOL FROM A DRAWER AND REACHED FOR THE DOOR, THROWING IT OPEN WIDE TO FIND...

SUCH A MESS! THAT'S THE ONLY TROUBLE WITH THIS 'CREEPING DEAD' VENEGEANCE BIT-SOMETIMES YOU MIGHT WAIT A BIT... TOO... LONG....

GOOD LORD!! CHOKE....!!

NAUSEOUS

PORTFOLIO

WRIGHTSON '70

© 1978 BERNI WRIGHTSON